GREAT MINDS® WIT & WISDOM

Grade 6 Module 1:
Resilience in the Great Depression

Student Edition

Copyright © 2016 Great Minds®

COPYRIGHT STATEMENT

Published by Great Minds®.

Copyright ©2016 Great Minds®. All rights reserved. No part of this work may be reproduced or used in any form or by any means—graphic, electronic, or mechanical, including photocopying or information storage and retrieval systems—without written permission from the copyright holder.

ISBN: 978-1-68386-041-9

STUDENT EDITION

GRADE 6 MODULE 1

Student Resources

Handout 1A: Fluency Practice 1

Handout 1B: Frayer Model

Handout 2A: Model Fluency Annotation

Handout 2B: ToSEEC Paragraph Model

Handout 2C: Transitional Words and Phrases

Handout 2D: Experiment with Transitional Words and Phrases

Handout 3A: Evidence Organizer—Analyze Bud's Reactions

Handout 4A: Evidence Organizer—Analyze Bud and Mama's Responses

Handout 6A: Fluency Practice 2

Handout 6B: Experiment with Evidence in a ToSEEC Paragraph

Handout 7A: Experiment with Elaboration in a ToSEEC Paragraph

Handout 8A: Figurative Language

Handout 9A: Evidence Organizer—"GM Sit-Down Strike"

Handout 10A: Examining Slang and Idiom in *Bud, Not Buddy*

Handout 11A: Evidence Organizer—Analyzing Bud's Actions

Handout 12A: Four Types of Disagreements

Handout 13A: Evidence Organizer—Compare and Contrast Events

Handout 13B: Exemplar Explanatory Essay

Handout 14A: Jazz and Strategic Disagreement

Handout 15A: Speaking and Listening Process Checklist

Handout 15B: Socratic Seminar Note Sheet

Handout 15C: Group Word-Solving Process

Handout 17A: Evidence Organizer—Analyze *Migrant Mother*

Handout 18A: Web Catcher Directions and Example

Handout 18B: Setting and Character in *Out of the Dust*

Handout 19A: Figurative Language and Imagery in *Out of the Dust*

Handout 19B: Sufficient Evidence

Handout 20A: Introduction to Sentence Variety

Handout 21A: Evidence Organizer—Central Ideas Put Forward by Texts

Handout 21B: Varying Sentences

Copyright © 2016 Great Minds®

Handout 21C: Tips for Enhancing Sentence Variety

Handout 22A: Fluency Practice 3

Handout 23A: Evidence Organizer—Themes in *Out of the Dust*

Handout 23B: Integrating Evidence

Handout 24A: Evidence Organizer—Billie Jo's Journey Processing Hardship and Hope

Handout 24B: Experiment with Formal Style I

Handout 25A: Evidence Organizer—Hardship's Impact on Billie Jo's Relationships

Handout 27A: Fluency Practice 4

Handout 29A: Speaking and Listening Process Checklist

Handout 30A: End-of-Module Task Organizer

Handout 30B: Fragments

Handout 32A: Experiment with Formal Style II

Volume of Reading Reflection Questions

Wit & Wisdom Parent Tip Sheet

Copyright © 2016 Great Minds®

Name _____

Date _____ Class _____

Handout 1A: Fluency Practice 1

Directions:
1. Day 1: Read the text carefully and annotate to help you read fluently.
2. Each day:
   a. Practice reading the text three to five times.
   b. Evaluate your progress by placing a √+, √, or √- in each unshaded box.
   c. Ask someone (adult or peer) to listen and evaluate you as well.
3. Last day: Respond to the self-reflection questions.

The door shut behind them and I heard a key jiggle in the lock. I plugged the right side of my nose and tried real hard to blow the smell of rubber out of the left side. The key jiggled in the lock again. This time when the door opened Mr. Amos was standing with Mrs. Amos. He was carrying my suitcase. Uh-oh, they'd looked inside. I could tell because the twine that held it together was tied in a kind of knot that I didn't know. This was wrong. They'd promised they'd keep it safe and not look in it. They'd laughed at me when I made them promise: but they did promise (Curtis, 14).

Student Performance Checklist:	Day 1		Day 2		Day 3		Day 4	
	You	Listener*	You	Listener*	You	Listener*	You	Listener*
Accurately read the passage 3–5 times.								
Read with appropriate phrasing and pausing.	▓	▓						
Read with appropriate expression.	▓	▓	▓					
Read articulately at a good pace and an audible volume.	▓	▓	▓	▓	▓	▓		

*Adult or peer

Self-reflection: What choices did you make when deciding how to read this passage, and why? What would you like to improve on or try differently next time?

Copyright © 2016 Great Minds®

Name _____

Date _____ Class _____

Handout 1B: Frayer Model

Directions: Complete the model for the designated word.

Definition:	Characteristics:
Examples:	**Non-Examples:**

Word:

Copyright © 2016 Great Minds®

Name _____

Date _____ Class _____

Handout 2A: Model Fluency Annotation

The following excerpt is from pages 4–5 of *Bud, Not Buddy*:

Most folks think you start to be a real adult when you're fifteen or sixteen years old, but that's not true, it really starts when you're around six. It's at six that grown folks don't think you're a cute little kid anymore, they talk to you and expect that you understand everything they mean. And you'd best understand too, if you aren't looking for some real trouble, 'cause it's around six that grown folks stop giving you little swats and taps and jump clean up to giving you slugs that'll knock you right down and have you seeing stars in the middle of the day. The first foster home I was in taught me that real quick.

1. Listen to the excerpt as it is read aloud. Use colored pens/pencils or highlighters to mark the **phrasing** used. You can use any system that makes sense to you for your annotations (e.g., swoop marks, brackets, highlighting of phrasing or punctuation).

Reflection: How are your annotations similar to and different from your partner's? Your teacher's?

_____

_____

_____

2. Listen again to the excerpt as it is read aloud. Use colored pens/pencils or highlighters to mark the **expression** used. You can use any system that makes sense to you for your annotations (e.g., punctuation, happy or sad faces, or underlining).

Reflection: What emotions are being conveyed by this passage? Which words or phrases in the text indicate these emotions?

_____

_____

_____

Copyright © 2016 Great Minds®

Name _____

Date _____ Class _____

3. Listen again to the excerpt as it is read aloud. What do you notice about the **articulation**, **pacing**, and **volume**?

_____

_____

_____

Copyright © 2016 Great Minds®

Name _____

Date _____ Class _____

Handout 2B: ToSEEC Paragraph Model

1. Write down what you think the function of each part of ToSEEC paragraph might be given its name:

Abbr.	Name	Function
ToS	Topic Statement	
E	Evidence	
E	Elaboration	
C	Concluding Statement	

2. Review the labeled sample ToSEEC paragraph below. After reviewing the paragraph and the labeling of the parts, go back and revise or add to your notes about the function of each part of a ToSEEC paragraph.

ToSEEC Sample 1

(TOPIC STATEMENT) Bud's main hardship in chapter 2 of Bud, Not Buddy is protecting himself. (EVIDENCE) Bud has to defend himself when Todd bullies him by throwing a punch and "Todd [falls] to the ground like he [has] been coldcocked" (13). (ELABORATION) Bud will not let anyone abuse or insult him. (EVIDENCE) However, Bud also knows that "being this brave [is] kind of stupid" (13) and hides under the bed to get away from Todd before he gets badly hurt. (ELABORATION) Bud defends himself by fighting back until he realizes that he can't win the fight. (CONCLUDING STATEMENT) Bud protects himself by being both brave and smart.

Copyright © 2016 Great Minds®

Name

Date   Class

3. Revise your Quick Write into the ToSEEC paragraph format below:

_____

_____

_____

_____

_____

_____

_____

_____

4. Compose a possible topic statement for the sample ToSEEC paragraph about Bud below.

ToSEEC Sample 2

(TOPIC STATEMENT):

_____

_____

_____

(Evidence) Bud is terrified of the stain in the shed that Todd has said is the blood of "the last kid who got put in [the shed]" who was never found (18). (ELABORATION) Bud fights to control his breathing and closes his eyes so that he doesn't feel so scared. He ends up calming himself down. (EVIDENCE) Bud faces his greatest fear when he thinks he sees "up at the very top of the shed...the biggest vampire bat you'd ever see" (25–26). (ELABORATION) Bud fights to control his fear by making himself not run from it. He attacks the bat bravely and although he is stung by hornets, he uses all the strength he has and is able to escape the shed.

Name _____

Date _____ Class _____

Handout 2C: Transitional Words and Phrases

If the sentence	Try one of these transitions:	
adds more evidence or ideas to the previous sentence or paragraph...	• furthermore • also • in addition	• even more • next • first, second, etc.
has an important time relationship to the previous sentence...	• immediately • afterward • earlier • later • soon • meanwhile	• sometimes • in the meantime • during • until now • next • then
provides an example to illustrate an idea from the previous sentence...	• for example • to illustrate • to demonstrate	• for instance • in fact
compares ideas of the previous sentence or paragraph...	• in the same way • similarly • likewise	
contrasts ideas of the previous sentence or paragraph...	• yet • but • nevertheless • nonetheless • after all • however	• otherwise • despite this • on the contrary • in contrast • on the other hand
clarifies or explains ideas from the previous sentence in another way...	• in other words • to explain • to clarify	• that is to say • to rephrase it • to put it another way
has a cause-and-effect relationship between the previous sentence...	• because • since • on account of • therefore	• consequently • thus • as a result
sums up or concludes the paragraph or essay...	• to summarize • to sum up • in short • in the end	• in summary • in conclusion • finally

Copyright © 2016 Great Minds®

Name _____

Date _____   Class _____

Handout 2D: Experiment with Transitional Words and Phrases

Directions: For each sentence pair, identify the relationship and insert an appropriate transition.

1. Bud fights to control his breathing. _____ he closes his eyes so that he doesn't feel so scared.

Relationship:

_____

2. Bud faces his greatest fear when he thinks he sees a vampire bat. _____ he controls his fear by making himself not run from it.

Relationship:

_____

3. Bud is stung by hornets. _____ he keeps fighting.

Relationship:

_____

4. Bud uses all his strength. _____ he is able to escape the shed.

Relationship:

_____

Copyright © 2016 Great Minds®

Name _____

Date _____ Class _____

Handout 3A: Evidence Organizer–Analyze Bud's Reactions

Directions: Complete the table. Find events and reactions in chapters 3 and 4 that reveal information about Bud's character.

Event	Bud's Reaction/Response	What This Reveals About Bud's Character
Chapter 1: Bud's mother died when he was six (4).		
Chapter 2: Todd lies to his mother and says Bud attacked him (11).		
Chapter 3:		
Chapter 4:		

Complete this 3-2-1:

3 words that describe Bud:

_____

_____

2 questions you have about Bud:

_____

_____

1 event that revealed the most about Bud's character:

_____

Copyright © 2016 Great Minds®

Name _____

Date _____ Class _____

Handout 4A: Evidence Organizer–Analyze Bud and Mama's Responses

Directions: Complete the chart with evidence from the text and your own inferences.

Event	Bud or Mama's Reaction	What This Reveals About Bud or Mama
	"You might be able to say that the Amoses were some mean old nosy folks, but you couldn't call them thieves" (38).	
	Mama looked like "she wished she could've emptied [the six-shooter pistols] on somebody" (39).	
Bud and his mother had the same conversations over and over again.		
Mama tells Bud that "when one door closes, don't worry, because another door opens" (43).		

Copyright © 2016 Great Minds®

Complete a 3-2-1:

3 things revealed about Bud in his reactions in chapter 5:

_____

_____

2 things revealed about Mama in her reactions in chapter 5:

_____

_____

1 question you have about Bud or Mama's character:

_____

Name

Date   Class

Handout 6A: Fluency Practice 2

Directions:

1. Day 1: Read the text carefully and annotate to help you read fluently.
2. Each day:
   a. Practice reading the text three to five times.
   b. Evaluate your progress by placing a √+, √, or √- in each unshaded box.
   c. Ask someone (adult or peer) to listen and evaluate you as well.
3. Last day: Respond to the self-reflection questions.

A man was yelling, "You yellow-bellied lowlifes, you waited until you knew most of the men were gone, you cowards!"

The cops wouldn't talk or nothing, they just kept piling Flint's Hooverville into the fire.

I tried to see if I could spot Deza Malone but there were too many people.

It seemed like the only good thing that came out of going to Hooverville was that I finally kissed a girl. Maybe someone was trying to tell me something, what with me missing the train and the blue flyer floating back to me, maybe Deza Malone was right.

Maybe I should stay here in Flint (Curtis, 86).

Student Performance Checklist:	Day 1		Day 2		Day 3		Day 4	
	You	Listener*	You	Listener*	You	Listener*	You	Listener*
Accurately read the passage 3–5 times.								
Read with appropriate phrasing and pausing.								
Read with appropriate expression.								
Read articulately at a good pace and an audible volume.								

*Adult or peer

Self-reflection: What choices did you make when deciding how to read this passage, and why? What would you like to improve on or try differently next time?

Copyright © 2016 Great Minds®

Name _____

Date _____   Class _____

Handout 6B: Experiment with Evidence in a ToSEEC Paragraph

Directions: For the given topic statement, provide evidence and citations in the graphic organizer.

Topic Statement: During the Great Depression, the American Dream wasn't the same for everyone.	
Evidence: Citation:	Elaboration:
Evidence: Citation:	Elaboration:
Concluding Statement:	

Name _____

Date _____ Class _____

Handout 7A: Experiment with Elaboration in a ToSEEC Paragraph

Directions: Complete the graphic organizer for the given topic statement, adding elaboration for the provided evidence and a concluding statement.

Topic Statement:	
The Hoovervilles of the Great Depression showed that working together yields positive outcomes.	
Evidence: Bud and Bugs were welcome to eat the stew in the Hooverville "but [they] all pitch in [there]" so "[they did] the cleanup after everyone's had their fill" (69). Citation: (69)	**Elaboration:**
Evidence: The Hooverville in St. Louis "was funded by private donations" and was "one of the country's largest and longest-standing Hoovervilles" ("Hoovervilles"). Citation: ("Hoovervilles")	**Elaboration:**
Concluding Statement:	

Copyright © 2016 Great Minds®

Name _____

Date _____ Class _____

Handout 8A: Figurative Language

Directions: Complete the chart using figurative language from the text and your analysis. Remember to cite page numbers.

Figurative language	What does this mean?	What does this reveal about the character?
The man never let go of my arm and wrestled the box [of blood] over into the backseat. If he would've let go of my arm for one second I would've run like the devil was chasing me (106).		

Copyright © 2016 Great Minds®

Name _____

Date _____ Class _____

Handout 9A: Evidence Organizer–"GM Sit-Down Strike"

Directions: Respond to questions 1-3 below before watching the video and then again after, and then complete questions 4 and 5 after our class discussion.

1. What does, "Once you pass the gates of General Motors, forget about the United States Constitution" mean?

My Initial Thoughts	New Ideas

2. How did factory owners and foremen respond to the strike?

My Initial Thoughts	New Ideas

Copyright © 2016 Great Minds®

Name _____

Date _____ Class _____

3. How were the GM workers able to win their rights?

My Initial Thoughts	New Ideas

4. Describe two new ideas presented by others in the discussion that you hadn't thought of.

_____

_____

5. Did your group meet your group discussion goal? Why or why not?

_____

_____

Copyright © 2016 Great Minds®

Name _____

Date _____   Class _____

Handout 10A: Examining Slang and Idiom in *Bud, Not Buddy*

Directions: Complete the table for the given examples of slang or idiom. Then add additional examples from anywhere in the book. The first row provides an example for you.

Slang or Idiom	Page Number	Meaning	Words or phrases that mean the same thing
"on the lam"	133	"escape or flee, especially from the police"	on the run
"copper"	133		
"rub me out"	137		
"what in the Sam Hill"	150		
"stuff your craw"	160		

Name _____

Date _____ Class _____

Handout 11A: Evidence Organizer–Analyzing Bud's Actions

Directions: Complete the first table while reading chapter 14 for homework. Add any questions you have to the second box.

Bud's Actions	What This Reveals About Bud
Bud considers telling Ms. Thomas that he's been bitten by a vampire but "something told [him] to tell the truth this time. [He] said, "That's just some hornet stings, ma'am" (163).	Bud is honest with the members of the band. He wants them to know who he truly is. It's important to him not to lie to them like he lied to the Amoses.

Questions I have about events in these chapters:

Copyright © 2016 Great Minds®

Name _____

Date _____ Class _____

Complete this table during your small-group discussion in the next lesson.

My Initial Thoughts	New Ideas

Copyright © 2016 Great Minds®

Name _____

Date _____ Class _____

Handout 12A: Four Types of Disagreements

Disagreement of Attitude

This is when both people agree on the facts, but feel differently about them. For example, imagine two people walked into a kitchen and reported what they saw. The first exclaimed, "The kitchen was a sloppy mess! There was food strewn everywhere." The second exclaimed, "What a productive room! There was evidence of delicious cooking everywhere." While both people saw the same space, they had very different interpretations of what they saw. With this type of disagreement, it is best to use neutral language to help others see the situation and draw their own conclusions. Both people would agree with the neutral statement, "There were drips of soup on the counter by the stove."

Disagreement of Definition

This kind of disagreement happens when two people use the same word or words, but have different meanings in mind. In the same kitchen, one person said, "The large appliance was white." The other person said, "The large appliance was silver." Who was right? They both were! The first person was referring to the refrigerator, while the second person was referring to the stove. With this type of disagreement, it is best to clarify the common term. In this case, they were using the word appliance to mean two different objects.

Disagreement of Fact

This type of disagreement happens when two people disagree on a fact. Going back to the kitchen scene, one person said, "There were two pies cooling on the counter." The other person said, "There were three pies cooling on the counter." With this type of disagreement, it is best to go back to the evidence. They both pull out their phones to show the pictures they took in the kitchen. The first person's picture shows a part of the counter with two pies cooling on it. The second person's picture shows the entire counter, and you can see a third pie in the back. Examining both pieces of evidence, both now agree that there were three pies on the counter.

Disagreement of Logic

This type of disagreement happens when people disagree with the logic or reasoning of an argument. In our kitchen example, let's say that both people who visited the kitchen agreed that all the pots in the kitchen had black handles. Picture evidence shows this to be a fact. The first person says, "There was a pot on the stove in the kitchen." The group uses logic to conclude that the pot on the stove had a black handle. The second person says, "There was a spatula in the kitchen that had a black handle. Therefore, it must be a pot, too." The group disagrees with the second person's logic because while it is true that all pots have black handles, it is not necessarily true in reverse. If something has a black handle, it isn't necessarily a pot. With this type of disagreement, it is best to examine the thinking together to come to an agreement.

Copyright © 2016 Great Minds®

Name _____

Date _____ Class _____

Handout 13A: Evidence Organizer—Compare and Contrast Events

Directions: Compare and contrast Bud's experience sleeping in the shed at the Amoses' with the night he spends in the little girl's room. List similarities in the center, differences in each of the outer spaces.

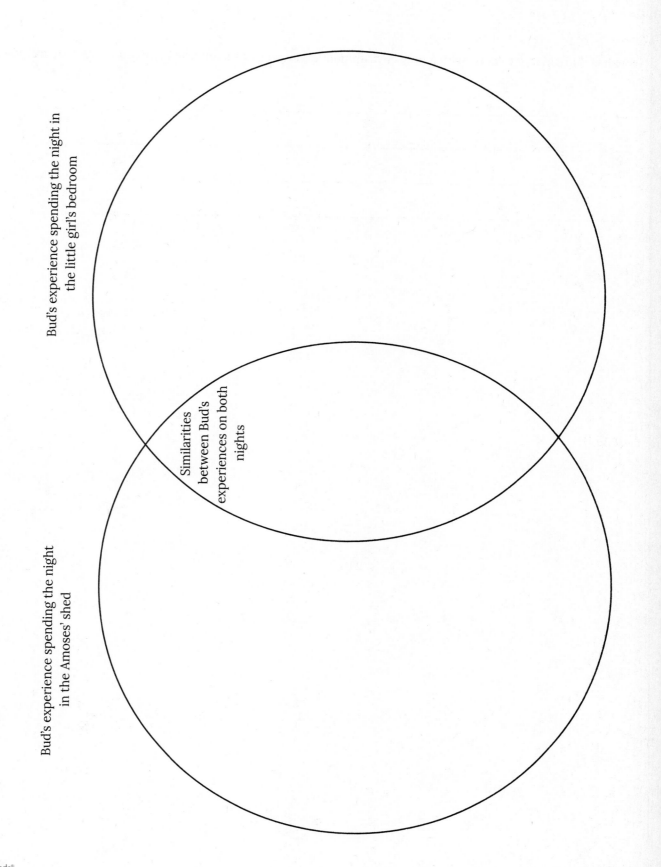

Bud's experience spending the night in the little girl's bedroom

Similarities between Bud's experiences on both nights

Bud's experience spending the night in the Amoses' shed

Copyright © 2016 Great Minds®

How has Bud's ability to cope with a new environment changed since spending the night in the Amoses' shed?

_____

_____

_____

_____

Copyright © 2016 Great Minds®

Name _____

Date _____   Class _____

Handout 13B: Exemplar Explanatory Essay

The maxim "when one door closes, another door opens" applies to people's experiences during the Great Depression, a period lasting from 1929 until World War II. Many Americans during the Great Depression experienced some type of hardship, whether that meant a lost job, a lost farm or home, or an inability to feed or take care of their families. Because of these hardships, Americans had to adapt to loss and difficulty by finding a way to make something positive come from something negative. The communities built in Hoovervilles and the unions formed in factories show how the people of the Great Depression opened doors for themselves.

Unemployment and homelessness, two "closing" doors of the Great Depression, created shantytowns called Hoovervilles, which became home to many people. During this period, some "13 [million] to 15 million Americans were unemployed," ("Hoovervilles") and unemployment often caused homelessness. Because people could no longer pay their rent or mortgage, people were turned out of their homes with nowhere to go. Often young teenagers would leave their homes and become homeless, hoping to ease the burden they placed on their families. For some, Hoovervilles became their new home. Hoovervilles were "shantytowns that cropped up across the nation, primarily on the outskirts of major cities" ("Hoovervilles"). However, despite the conditions at the camps (for example, many people slept in shelters made out of cardboard boxes), Hoovervilles opened doors for people. Hoovervilles offered a sense of community; a migrant could find food and shelter, and most important, a sympathetic ear: "The one place where the young hobo was assured a welcome was the 'jungle,' as the hobo camps were called" (Uys). People helping people defined these "hobo camps" or Hoovervilles. In a time when everything was scarce, Hoovervilles offered people a place where generosity and compassion were practiced. Even though the door of a home had closed for some people, the door of community help had opened.

Poor labor conditions closed another door for people during the Great Depression, resulting in a door opening with the formation of unions. Manufacturer workers had "no rights" and could be fired for any reason ("GM Strike Video"). For example, people did not have job security if they got hurt at work; if they could not perform their job, a worker would simply be let go without pay. If a worker lost his job, often he would face additional hardships, like losing his home. Protected employment was a necessity for people so that they could depend on their wages to pay their bills and feed their families. As a result of this closed door, workers banded together to form unions, an action that resulted in opening doors for countless people. The union's purpose was for workers to help other workers. They helped each other by organizing "sit-downs" and bravely standing up to injustice, eventually securing workplace rights as a result of their protests and strikes. Because of their actions, "the auto worker became a different human being" ("GM Strike Video"). The people who formed unions and organized protests successfully opened doors for all future workers to have legal rights that could not be taken away by an employer.

Few periods in American history have been as catastrophic as the Great Depression was for so many millions. It closed doors for many, sometimes doors that would stay slammed shut. Yet for some, even with those closed doors of homelessness and unemployment, doors were opened. Sometimes, people found community and joined unions. For these people, the Great Depression was a positive and negative experience, where hardship was countered by the strength of the human spirit.

Copyright © 2016 Great Minds®

Name _____

Date _____ Class _____

ToSEEC Explanatory Essay Model

Introduction			
Hook			
Introduce			
Thesis & Preview			
Body Paragraph 1 *(Supporting Point 1)*		**Body Paragraph 2** *(Supporting Point 2)*	
Topic Statement:		Topic Statement:	
Evidence: Citation:	Elaboration:	Evidence: Citation:	Elaboration:
Evidence: Citation:	Elaboration:	Evidence: Citation:	Elaboration:
Concluding Statement:		Concluding Statement:	
Conclusion			

Copyright © 2016 Great Minds®

Name _____

Date _____ Class _____

Handout 14A: Jazz and Strategic Disagreement

1   Make a tally mark for every time you hear something that fits one of these descriptions.

"Instead of the horn making music it seemed like [the performer] made it talk" (200).	"Every time he patted the strings, it sounded like something wide and heavy was walking by slow and easy" (201).	"[The singer] was saying things like "La da de da…ha whee a day," then [the saxophonist] would answer on the saxophone and… the two of them were having a regular conversation" (202).	"The piano sound[ed] like water hitting big rocks" (202).

2.   Why did Bud enjoy listening to the band play jazz?

_____

_____

_____

3.   Make a tally mark for every time you hear one of the types of strategic disagreement.

Disagreements of Fact	Disagreements of Definition	Disagreements of Logic	Disagreements of Attitude

4.   How did strategic disagreement impact today's discussion?

_____

_____

_____

Copyright © 2016 Great Minds®

Name _____

Date _____   Class _____

Handout 15A: Speaking and Listening Process Checklist

Grade 6 Speaking and Listening Process Checklist	Self +/ Δ	Peer +/ Δ	Teacher +/ Δ
I used text evidence to support my opinion.			
I asked questions.			
I followed all the rules for speaking in a group.			
I set and met my participation goal.			
I built and elaborated on comments from my peers.			
I agreed and disagreed respectfully and strategically.			
▪ I used a polite tone of voice throughout the discussion.			
▪ I used my knowledge of why people disagree to resolve disagreements.			
I stayed engaged in the conversation the whole time.			
I brought the conversation back on topic when needed.			

1. What is your goal for today's Socratic Seminar to improve your participation?

_____

_____

2. Did you meet your goal? Why or why not?

_____

_____

_____

3. What will your goal be for the next discussion?

_____

_____

Copyright © 2016 Great Minds®

Name _____

Date _____   Class _____

Handout 15B: Socratic Seminar Note Sheet

Directions: Write in ideas from the Socratic Seminar.

Ways That Bud Has Been Transformed

People Who Influenced Bud's Transformation	Experiences That Influenced Bud's Transformation

How has Bud changed since the beginning of the story?

_____

_____

_____

Copyright © 2016 Great Minds®

Name _____

Date _____ Class _____

Handout 15C: Group Word-Solving Process

Directions: Complete each step of the process for the designated word.

Group Word-Solving Process

WORD:	
1. Check if any group members know the word already.	
2. Check "outside" the word to see whether there are any clues in the text around it.	
3. Check "inside" the word to see whether there are clues from the root or affix.	
4. Check a reference, such as a thesaurus or dictionary.	
5. Check back in the text to confirm the meaning in the dictionary makes sense to the context.	

Copyright © 2016 Great Minds®

Name

Date   Class

Handout 17A: Evidence Organizer–Analyze *Migrant Mother*

1. Complete the Notice and Wonder table as you view the photograph.

I Notice...	I Wonder...

Copyright © 2016 Great Minds®

Name _____

Date _____ Class _____

2. Discuss each question with your group members and record ideas.

A. How does Dorothea Lange hold your attention while viewing this photo?	B. How does Lange use composition?
C. How does Lange use texture (the feel or look of a surface)?	**D. When Lange was taking these photographs, color photography was too complicated and difficult for use on the road. How did Lange use light and contrast in her black-and-white photograph?**

Copyright © 2016 Great Minds®

Name _____

Date _____ Class _____

3. In a ToSEEC paragraph, explain what is conveyed by *Migrant Mother*.

_____

_____

_____

_____

_____

_____

_____

_____

_____

_____

_____

_____

_____

_____

_____

_____

_____

_____

_____

_____

_____

_____

_____

Copyright © 2016 Great Minds®

Name

Date   Class

Handout 18A: Web Catcher Directions and Example

The purpose of a Web Catcher is to:

1. catch details that reveal potentially important information;
2. infer what the significance of these details might be;
3. ask questions about these details; and
4. examine how these details connect with one other.

Directions: At the center of the web is a circle that provides the focus of the catching (e.g., a poem title, a character name, a literary element like setting). As you gather quotations and examples from the text about the focus, draw lines and circles to record the information as well as your inferences and questions. Also consider connections among circles and draw lines (threads) to show those connections.

Below is an example of a Web Catcher that focuses on the gist of the poem "Beginning: August 1920" (3–5).

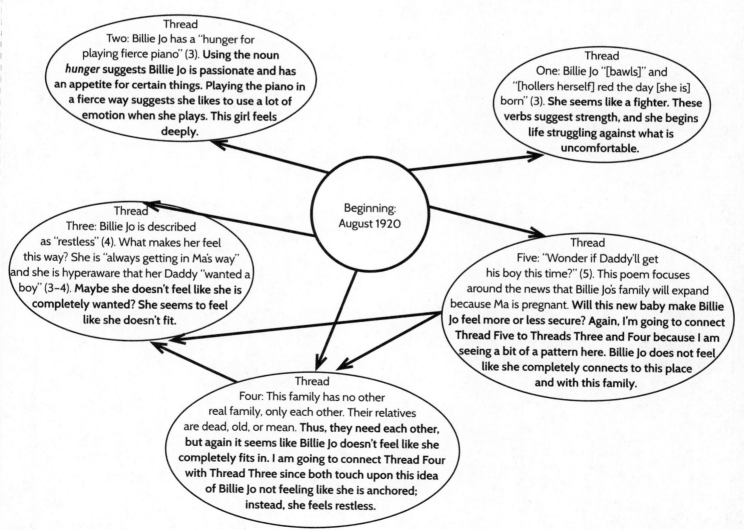

Name _____

Date _____ Class _____

Handout 18B: Setting and Character in *Out of the Dust*

Directions: For each organizer below, finish the topic statement that has been provided and then add appropriate evidence, citations, and elaboration.

Topic Statement:
The details in the first three poems help convey the setting of the book as a place where _____ _____

Evidence:	Elaboration:
Citation:	

Evidence:	Elaboration:
Citation:	

Copyright © 2016 Great Minds®

Name _____

Date _____ Class _____

Topic Statement:

The details in the first three poems help convey Billie Jo as a character who _____

_____ .

Evidence:	Elaboration:
Citation:	

Evidence:	Elaboration:
Citation:	

Copyright © 2016 Great Minds®

Name _____

Date _____ Class _____

Handout 19A: Figurative Language and Imagery in *Out of the Dust*

Directions: For each organizer below, add appropriate evidence, citations, and elaboration for the given topic statement.

Topic Statement:
Figurative language and imagery develop Billie Jo's love of the piano.

Evidence from "On Stage"	**Elaboration:**
Citation:	

Evidence from "On Stage"	**Elaboration:**
Citation:	

Copyright © 2016 Great Minds®

Name _____

Date _____ Class _____

Topic Statement:
Figurative language and imagery develop Billie Jo's love of the piano.

Evidence from "Dazzled"	Elaboration:
Citation:	

Evidence from "Dazzled"	Elaboration:
Citation:	

Copyright © 2016 Great Minds®

Name _____

Date _____ Class _____

Handout 19B: Sufficient Evidence

Topic Statement: Figurative language develops Billie Jo's love of the piano.

Evidence and Elaboration Example 1:
When Billie Jo plays the piano, she compares the experience to what "heaven" must resemble, since "[i]t's the best / [she has] ever felt" (13–14). This metaphor emphasizes that playing piano makes Billie Jo feel incredibly happy and fulfilled.

Evidence and Elaboration Example 2:
When Billie Jo plays, she "[sizzles] with / Mad Dog, / swinging with the Black Mesa Boys" (13). The figurative language of "sizzling" and "swinging" with the band shows how much fun Billie Jo has as she plays. For example, "sizzling" depicts Billie Jo and Mad Dog on fire as they play. They are consumed with the music. The imagery used to describe the crowd also develops Billie Jo's love of piano. They "sway in the / Palace aisles / grinning and stomping" with their "fingers snapping, / feet tapping" (13). This imagery depicts the crowd reacting to Billie Jo's music enthusiastically, and she loves their energy. Playing for these folks makes her feel alive and powerful.

Copyright © 2016 Great Minds®

Name _____

Date _____   Class _____

Handout 20A: Introduction to Sentence Variety

Directions: Review the sentences used in each sample.

We sat taking our six-weeks test. The wind rose. The sand blew right through the cracks in the schoolhouse wall. The sand blew right through the gaps around the window glass. The tests were finally done. We were all coughing pretty good. We all needed a bath. I hope we get bonus points for testing in a dust storm.	While we sat taking our six-weeks test, the wind rose and the sand blew right through the cracks in the schoolhouse wall, right through the gaps around the window glass, and by the time the tests were done, each and every one of us was coughing pretty good and we all needed a bath. I hope we get bonus points for testing in a dust storm. (Hesse, 37)

Copyright © 2016 Great Minds®

Name _____

Date _____   Class _____

Handout 21A: Evidence Organizer–Central Ideas Put Forward by Texts

Directions: Complete the table to track the central ideas put forward by the texts.

What sustained people during the Great Depression?		
Central Idea	**Evidence**	**Elaboration**
Generosity	Edgar Bledsoe in the article "Hoover's Prodigal Children: Hungry Times on Mean Streets" rode the rails out of desperation. He was starving. Out of the goodness of their hearts, total strangers gave him and his friends food. Edgar benefitted because of thess men's generosity.	Kids like Edgar felt like they were taken care of by strangers. Instead of feeling completely alone and helpless, these kids had someone looking after them. The kindness and generosity people showed each other helped sustain everyone's spirits because people believed that somewhere, someone would extend a helping hand if needed.
	In *Out of the Dust*, Ma constantly gives to such strangers. Even though Billie Jo's family is poor, Ma manages to still donate both food and clothing for charitable causes. When a boy comes to their house and "[asks] for food," Ma "[sits] him down/and [gives] him biscuits/and milk" (Hesse, 58). She knows that somewhere out there "his mother is worrying about him" and "wishing her boy would come home" (59).	Ma sees her own child in the "wild boy of the road," and she cannot turn him away (59). Because of Billie Jo's family's generosity, the nameless boy is able to survive without a home or family to take care of him, and Ma benefits from her own generosity because it makes her feel like she is helping someone just like herself.

Name _____

Date _____ Class _____

Copyright © 2016 Great Minds®

Name _____

Date _____ Class _____

Handout 21B: Varying Sentences

Directions: Read the following paragraph aloud, and respond to the questions with a partner.

Ma constantly gives to such strangers in *Out of the Dust*. Ma donates both food and clothing for charitable causes. Ma does this even though the family is poor. Ma "[sits] him down/and [gives] him biscuits/and milk" when a boy comes to the house (58). She knows that somewhere out there "his mother is worrying about him" and "wishing her boy would come home" (59). Ma sees her own child in the "wild boy of the road" (59). She cannot turn him away (59).

1. What do you notice about the lengths of the sentences? How does that impact your reading and understanding of the paragraph?

_____

_____

_____

_____

2. What do you notice about the structures of the sentences? How does that impact your reading and understanding of the paragraph?

_____

_____

_____

_____

3. What do you notice about the subjects of the sentences? How does that impact your reading and understanding of the paragraph?

_____

_____

_____

_____

Copyright © 2016 Great Minds®

Name _____

Date _____ Class _____

4. What do you notice about how the sentences show relationships among one? How does that impact your reading and understanding of the paragraph?

_____

_____

_____

_____

5. How would you revise this paragraph to improve the sentence variety to make it more effective and better convey meaning?

_____

_____

_____

_____

Copyright © 2016 Great Minds®

Name

Date   Class

Handout 21C: Tips for Enhancing Sentence Variety

- Break a sentence up into shorter sentences to create a stronger "punch."

- Rearrange the order of the words in the sentence to make the writing more interesting.

- Combine sentences into one long sentence to show connections among ideas.

- Change the subject of the sentence to create a better flow.

- Use transition words to demonstrate the relationships among ideas.

Copyright © 2016 Great Minds®

Name _____

Date _____ Class _____

Handout 22A: Fluency Practice 3

Directions:

1. Day 1: Read the text carefully and annotate to help you read fluently.
2. Each day:
   a. Practice reading the text three to five times.
   b. Evaluate your progress by placing a √+, √, or √- in each unshaded box.
   c. Ask someone (adult or peer) to listen and evaluate you as well.
3. Last day: Respond to the self-reflection questions.

The Path of Our Sorrow

Miss Freeland said,
"During the Great War we fed the world.
We couldn't grow enough wheat
to fill all the bellies.
The price the world paid for our wheat
was so high
it swelled our wallets
and our heads,
and we bought bigger tractors,
more acres,
until we had mortgages
and rent
and bills
beyond reason,
but we all felt so useful, we didn't notice.
Then the war ended and before long,
Europe didn't need our wheat anymore,
they could grow their own.
But we needed Europe's money
to pay our mortgage,
our rent,
our bills.
We squeezed more cattle,
more sheep,
onto less land,
and they grazed down the stubble
till they reached root.
And the price of wheat kept dropping
so we had to grow more bushels
to make the same amount of money we made before,
to pay for all that equipment, all that land,
and the more sod we plowed up,
the drier things got,
because the water that used to collect there
under the grass, biding its time,

Copyright © 2016 Great Minds®

Name _____

Date _____ Class _____

keeping things alive through the dry spells
wasn't there anymore.
Without the sod the water vanished,
the soil turned to dust.
Until the wind took it,
lifting it up and carrying it away.
Such a sorrow doesn't come suddenly,
there are a thousand steps to take
before you get there."
But now,
sorrow climbs up our front steps,
big as Texas, and we didn't even see it coming,
even though it'd been making its way straight for us
all along.

September 1934
(Hesse, 83–84)

Student Performance Checklist:	Day 1		Day 2		Day 3		Day 4	
	You	Listener*	You	Listener*	You	Listener*	You	Listener*
Accurately read the passage 3–5 times.								
Read with appropriate phrasing and pausing.								
Read with appropriate expression.								
Read articulately at a good pace and an audible volume.								

*Adult or peer

Self-reflection: What choices did you make when deciding how to read this passage, and why? What would you like to improve on or try differently next time?

Copyright © 2016 Great Minds®

Name _____

Date _____ Class _____

Handout 23A: Evidence Organizer—Themes in *Out of the Dust*

Directions: Complete the row of analysis for your group's assigned theme. When the class reconvenes and other groups share out, record at least two other groups' analysis of other themes in the additional blank rows.

Evidence *Record any words, thoughts, or actions that reveal or develop your assigned theme.*	Elaboration *Provide elaboration about how this piece of evidence conveys this theme.*	Effect on Character *How is the character's perspective impacted, shaped, or altered by this theme? In other words, how does _____ affect the way a character thinks and feels?*	Thematic Message *At this point in the story, what possible message is being conveyed about this theme? Compose a thematic message.*
Despair "Only Arley Wanderdale talks about them, / and how they could play piano again, / if I would only try" (89).	Billie Jo feels an overwhelming sense of loss because of the injury to her hands. She once felt very proud of her hands; her skill at using them to play piano made her feel confident and talented, and they connected her to her Ma. Now she feels only despair when she thinks about them because she views them as permanently damaged. She does not share Arley Wanderdale's belief that she can play again.	Despair makes Billie Jo feel like she can never again do what she once loved: play the piano. Despair over her Ma's death and despair over the pain in her hands leave her feeling hopeless. As a result, her perspective of her future changes. She does not believe it includes music.	People need something with which to counterbalance despair, something like hope.
Your group's assigned theme (_____):			
A peer group's theme (_____):			
A peer group's theme (_____):			

Copyright © 2016 Great Minds®

Name _____

Date _____   Class _____

Handout 23B: Integrating Evidence

Strategy	Example
Use a complete sentence followed by a colon to introduce a quotation that consists of one or more independent clauses.	Billie Jo believes that Coach Albright no longer asks her to join his basketball team because of her injured hands: "Coach Albright [doesn't] say anything to me about / basketball this year. / I haven't gotten any shorter. / It's because of my hands" (89).
Use an introductory phrase followed by a comma to introduce a quotation that consists of one or more independent clauses.	According to Billie Jo, "[Mad Dog] doesn't stare at [her] deformed hands. / He looks at [her] like [she] is / someone he knows" (92).
Use just a word or phrase from the text and incorporate it into your own sentence.	When Billie Jo asks her father a question about Mad Dog's real name, he "looks at [her] like [she is] talking in another language" (93).
Incorporate a quotation at the beginning, middle, or end of a sentence, or choose to divide it using your own words in the middle.	After seeing the art exhibit, Billie Jo "[feels] such a hunger to see such things," and she leaves angry "because [she] can't" (95).

Note: Use brackets any time you change language in the cited quotation. You should change the verb tense to present when discussing the plot of a fictional text, even if the text's tense is different.

Copyright © 2016 Great Minds®

Name _____

Date _____   Class _____

Handout 24A: Evidence Organizer–Billie Jo's Journey Processing Hardship and Hope

Poem	Hard Moment *Paraphrase example and/or cite evidence*	Elaboration	Hopeful Moment *Paraphrase example and/or cite evidence*	Elaboration
"Scrubbing up Dust" (109–110)	Ma's "haunting" deeply disturbs Billie Jo.	Billie Jo keeps thinking about her Ma and how her Ma would disapprove of the mud and dust in the house. Billie Jo wants to ignore it, but she can't because her Ma's memory and presence is very real (like a ghost that can be felt but not seen).	Ma's "haunting" reminds Billie Jo of her mother's stubborn nature. This is her stubborn nature, too. She is like her Ma.	Billie Jo might want to put distance between herself and her Ma's memory, but Ma's memory is as stubborn as the real Ma who would have done it all "with [her] brother Franklin to tend to" (110). She cannot escape how important her Ma was and is to her well-being, and she shouldn't. She needs to be haunted so that she doesn't just check out and give up.
"Outlined by Dust" (111–113)	Billie Jo's father "stares at her" and makes her feel uncomfortable.	Billie Jo's father repeatedly stares at his daughter, but he does not talk (111). It seems like he wants to reach out but can't, and neither can she. The wall between them is too large.	Billie Jo's father begins to sing, "even now, / even after so much sorrow."	Billie Jo's father has been completely depressed, staying silent and withdrawn from the world. Here he breaks his silence with music.
	"I can't make myself over the way Ma did. / And yet, if I could look in the mirror and see her in / my face. / If I could somehow know that Ma / and Baby Franklin / lived on in me… / But it can't be. / I'm my father's daughter."	Billie Jo knows that she can't change to make her father love her more (by seeing Ma in her). This makes her depressed.	"I can't make myself over the way Ma did. / And yet, if I could look in the mirror and see her in / my face. / If I could somehow know that Ma / and Baby Franklin / lived on in me… / But it can't be. / I'm my father's daughter."	Billie Jo realizes that she can feel better if she can find a way to see how Ma lives on inside her. She has identified what she needs to do in order to heal.

Copyright © 2016 Great Minds®

Name _____

Date _____ Class _____

Poem	Hard Moment *Paraphrase example and/ or cite evidence*	Elaboration	Hopeful Moment *Paraphrase example and/ or cite evidence*	Elaboration
"Birth" (123)				
"Dreams" (127–128)				

Copyright © 2016 Great Minds®

Name

Date   Class

Poem	Hard Moment *Paraphrase example and/ or cite evidence*	Elaboration	Hopeful Moment *Paraphrase example and/ or cite evidence*	Elaboration
"The Competition" (129–133)				
"The Piano Player" (134–135)				

Copyright © 2016 Great Minds®

Name _____

Date _____   Class _____

Handout 24B: Experiment with Formal Style I

Directions: Read the paragraph. Circle words that could be revised to enhance the formal style of the paragraph. Then, rewrite the paragraph in a more formal style on the lines below.

There weren't many other times as bad as the Great Depression for lots of people. Seeing shut doors all over the place. People lost homes and jobs! But sometimes other people helped people find new open doors.

_____

_____

_____

_____

_____

_____

_____

_____

_____

_____

_____

_____

_____

_____

_____

_____

Copyright © 2016 Great Minds®

Name _____

Date _____ Class _____

Handout 25A: Evidence Organizer–Hardship's Impact on Billie Jo's Relationships

Directions: Complete the table below to show how Billie Jo's relationship changes with people, places, and objects.

Billie Jo's relationship with...	What is this relationship like before the hardship(s) occur?	What hardships impact this relationship?	How and why does hardship alter the relationship?	
Mad Dog	She feels competitive with Mad Dog but in a friendly way. She doesn't completely mind that he is more talented; she is happy that she gets to play with him. She loves playing music with him. He is not only extremely talented but also cute; she has a bit of a crush on Mad Dog. She looks at Mad Dog and the rest of the musicians as a second family. She feels like this family has helped her find "her place in the world" (49).	Her Ma's death The disfigurement of her hands Her insecurity that she is not an equal to Mad Dog	Hardship alters their relationship by Billie Jo pulling away from Mad Dog and the rest of the musicians. Shortly after the accident, Billie Jo "never [goes] by Arley's anymore" and withdraws from Mad Dog because playing the piano is now a painful experience for her (155). She not only feels the physical pain in her hands when she plays, but she also feels emotional pain: she no longer views herself as any good, and she still associates the piano with her Ma. When Mad Dog asks about her hands, "[She crosses her] arms in front of [her]/ tight/ so [her] scars won't show" (155). This gesture lets him know that she wants distance. It is too painful for her to admit that her scarred hands have destroyed her dream of playing with the band. She just wants to be left alone with her grief. Mad Dog keeps trying to reach out to her, but he can tell that she is pulling away, and this makes him "[look] at [her] / halfway between picking a fight and kindness" (155). He doesn't know how to comfort her, and on their walks, "never says a word" (155). He does say goodbye when he leaves for Amarillo, but Billie Jo only feels more of a distance between them because he can leave–his hands are "scarless," meaning he has not been broken by anything–whereas she cannot (169).	
Her father				

Name _____

Date _____ Class _____

Billie Jo's relationship with...	What is this relationship like before the hardship(s) occur?	What hardships impact this relationship?	How and why does hardship alter the relationship?
The piano			
The land and her home			

Name _____

Date _____   Class _____

Handout 27A: Fluency Practice 4

Directions:

1. Day 1: Read the text carefully and annotate to help you read fluently.
2. Each day:
    a. Practice reading the text three to five times.
    b. Evaluate your progress by placing a √+, √, or √- in each unshaded box.
    c. Ask someone (adult or peer) to listen and evaluate you as well.
3. Last day: Respond to the self-reflection questions.

Thanksgiving List

Prairie birds, the whistle of gophers, the wind
blowing,
the smell of grass
and spicy earth,
friends like Mad Dog, the cattle down in the river,
water washing over their hooves,
the sky so
big, so full of
shifting clouds,
the cloud shadows creeping
over the fields,
Daddy's smile
and his laugh,
and his songs,
Louise,
food without dust,
Daddy seeing to Ma's piano,
newly cleaned and tuned,
the days when my hands don't hurt at all,
the thank-you note from Lucille in Moline, Kansas,
the sound of rain,
Daddy's hole staying full of water
as the windmill turns,
the smell of green,
of damp earth,
of hope returning to our farm.
The poppies set to
bloom on Ma and Franklin's grave,
the morning with the whole day waiting,
full of promise,
the night
of quiet, of no expectations, of rest.
And the certainty of home, the one I live in,
and the one
that lives in me.

(Hesse, 220-221)

Copyright © 2016 Great Minds®

Name _____

Date _____ Class _____

Student Performance Checklist:	Day 1		Day 2		Day 3		Day 4	
	You	Listener*	You	Listener*	You	Listener*	You	Listener*
Accurately read the passage 3–5 times.								
Read with appropriate phrasing and pausing.								
Read with appropriate expression.								
Read articulately at a good pace and an audible volume.								

*Adult or peer

Self-reflection: What choices did you make when deciding how to read this passage, and why? What would you like to improve on or try differently next time?

Name _____

Date _____ Class _____

Handout 29A: Speaking and Listening Process Checklist

Grade 6 Speaking and Listening Process Checklist			
	Self +/ Δ	Peer +/ Δ	Teacher +/ Δ
I used text evidence to support my opinion.			
I asked questions.			
I followed all the rules for speaking in a group.			
I set and met my participation goal.			
I built and elaborated on comments from my peers.			
I agreed and disagreed respectfully and strategically.			
▪ I used a polite tone of voice throughout the discussion.			
▪ I used my knowledge of why people disagree to resolve disagreements.			
I deferred politely to other speakers.			
▪ I listened respectfully to the ideas of others.			
▪ I helped others get a chance to speak.			
I stayed engaged in the conversation the whole time.			
I brought the conversation back on topic when needed.			

1. What is your goal for today's Socratic Seminar to improve your participation?

_____

_____

2. Did you meet your goal? Why or why not?

_____

_____

_____

Copyright © 2016 Great Minds®

Name _____

Date _____ Class _____

3. What will your goal be for the next discussion?

_____

_____

Statements and Questions	For Clarification or Paraphrasing
<ul><li>I wonder why…</li><li>What if we looked at this in a different way, such as…</li><li>What in the text makes you say that?</li><li>How does that support our idea about…</li><li>In my mind I see…</li><li>Based on…, I infer that…</li><li>Do you agree or disagree with…</li><li>I am still confused by…</li><li>*Based on…, I predict that…</li></ul>	<ul><li>Could you please rephrase that?</li><li>Can you say more about that?</li><li>I have a question about that…</li><li>Could someone please paraphrase that?</li><li>* In other words, are you saying ?</li></ul>
For Building Ideas	**For Different Viewpoint**
<ul><li>* I agree with and I'd like to add…</li><li>I really like that idea because…</li><li>That idea is important because…</li><li>If we change that a little, we can see…</li><li>* Another example of is…</li><li>This reminds me of…</li><li>Now I am wondering…</li><li>* This relates back to our essential question because…</li></ul>	<ul><li>That's a great point, but I think…</li><li>* I agree with the part about , but I think…</li><li>On the other hand, what about…</li><li>The evidence seems to suggest something different, such as…</li><li>* I politely disagree with because…</li></ul>
Partners	**Problem-Solving**
<ul><li>We decided that…</li><li>* During the Turn-and-Talk, pointed out to me that…</li><li>After our Think-Pair-Share, I believe I have a new idea…</li><li>We concluded that…</li></ul>	<ul><li>I think the way to continue is…</li><li>We should identify…</li><li>I think we should do this step by step starting with…</li><li>Another way to look at this is…</li><li>I feel like we are missing something because…</li><li>Maybe we can reframe this by…</li><li>Which thinking map could we use to help us?</li></ul>
Summarizing	**Other**
<ul><li>* I'd like to go back to what was saying and…</li><li>So, the big idea is…</li><li>So, what can we conclude from this?</li><li>After our analysis, it appears that…</li><li>Several things contributed to this conclusion; the most important was…</li></ul>	<ul><li></li><li></li><li></li><li></li><li></li></ul>

Copyright © 2016 Great Minds®

Name _____

Date _____ Class _____

Handout 3OA: End of Module Task Organizer

Step 1: EOM Evidence Organizers

BUD: *Bud, Not Buddy*

How would you describe the character and how he/she viewed the world and him-/herself at the **end of the novel**? In other words, how was this character transformed by his/her experiences throughout the text?

How would you describe the character and how he/she viewed the world and him/herself at the **start of this novel**?

Name _____

Date _____ Class _____

Hardships What hardship did the character face?	Responses How did the character respond to the hardship?	Characteristics What does this response reveal about the character? In other words, what do we learn about his/her character traits or characteristics?	Transformation? To what extent does this characteristic contribute to the character's resilience and transformation?

Name _____

Date _____ Class _____

BILLIE JO: *Out of the Dust*		
How would you describe the character and how he/she viewed the world and him-/herself at the **start of the novel?**	How would you describe the character and how he/she viewed the world and him-/herself at the **end of the novel?** In other words, how was this character transformed by his/her experiences throughout the text?	

Copyright © 2016 Great Minds®

Transformation? To what extent does this characteristic contribute to the character's resilience and transformation?		
Characteristics What does this response reveal about the character? In other words, what do we learn about his/her character traits or characteristics?		
Responses How did the character respond to the hardship?		
Hardships What hardship did the character face?		

Copyright © 2016 Great Minds®

Name _____

Date _____ Class _____

Step 2: EOM Exemplar Evidence Organizer

BAYARD KELBY: *Out of the Dust*	
How would you describe the character and how he/she viewed the world and him/herself at the **start of the novel**?	How would you describe the character and how he/she viewed the world and him-/herself at the **end of the novel**? In other words, how was this character transformed by his/her experiences throughout the text?
• Bayard won't accept that droughts have been ongoing; he keeps believing that rain will fall. • Bayard literally fights against the dust. He runs out into dust storms as if he can stop them. He doesn't cry when he can't. • Bayard refuses to change his farming methods. • Bayard gets drunk. He does not want to deal with the reality that Ma is dying. • Bayard's depression makes him stop desiring to be connected to people. Example 1: Bayard withdraws from Billie Jo. They no longer communicate after Ma's death; they live together in a silent house. His pain causes him to retreat into himself; he stops being a present father. Billie Jo feels like he is a stranger. • Bayard's depression makes him stop desiring to be connected to people. Example 2: Bayard withdraws from the world. He spends all his time silently digging a huge hole, presumably to create a man-made pond, and will not engage with others.	• Bayard makes peace with hardship. He changes his attitude about the best way to farm. Bayard realizes that he needs to listen to the land. He understands that he can't fight droughts or dust storms but needs to adapt. He becomes willing to change what and how he grows. At the end of the novel, he decides that he will plant other things besides wheat, and he will replant the grass like Ma wanted. • When Billie Jo runs away, Bayard realizes that he needs to start appreciating what he has and needs to communicate with his daughter. He does not want to lose her. • He learns how to forgive himself and his daughter for the accident. His trip to see a doctor about his cancerous skin spots indicates that he no longer wants to punish himself. He is ready to live again. • Bayard learns how to be a good parent. He goes to the doctor for Billie Jo, and he helps her around the house and opens his heart to her. He finds ways to reconnect with his daughter so that she knows that he loves her. He tells her stories of his past, and lets her know that he is proud of her. • Bayard learns how to re-create a sense of family with his daughter and with his new love, Louise. He learns how to open his heart and be vulnerable and loving. He no longer withdraws from the world.

Hardships	Responses	Characteristics	Transformation?
Droughts and dust storms	• At first, Bayard refuses to change his farming methods and fights against the dust storms.	• Stubborn • Refuses to change	NO
	• He changes his attitude about the best way to farm and realizes that he needs to listen to the land.	• Flexible • Adaptable	YES
The death of Ma	• At first, Bayard plunges into a deep depression and withdraws from the world and his daughter.	• Withdrawn • Avoids everything • Gives up	NO
	• When Billie Jo runs away, Bayard realizes that he needs to start appreciating what he has and needs to communicate with his daughter. He changes how he responds to Ma's absence; instead of pulling away from everyone, he learns how to reconnect and form new relationships with people.	• Takes responsibility • Appreciative • Open • Caring and loving parent	YES

Copyright © 2016 Great Minds®

Name

Date   Class

Step 2: EOM Exemplar Essay–Bayard Kelby

Losing a loved one is the worst type of hardship: it is a tragedy. The characters in Karen Hesse's novel *Out of the Dust* experience this type of tragedy; Billie Jo Kelby and her Daddy, Bayard, struggle to carry on after losing their beloved Ma in a fatal accident. Although Bayard Kelby initially withdraws from the world and his daughter after his wife's death, he is jolted awake when Billie Jo runs away. Not wanting to lose Billie Jo, Bayard transforms his broken life by forming new relationships with loved ones and the land. He creates these relationships by making peace with hardship and learning how to be a better parent.

Bayard transforms his life by beginning new relationships after he learns how to make peace with hardship. After his daughter runs away but chooses to return, Bayard realizes that he needs to appreciate what he has and not remain withdrawn from people by escaping into depression. In response, he no longer fights hardship or the past; he begins instead to accept that things have changed and move forward. For example, he begins to open his heart to another woman: Louise. Louise enriches both his and Billie Jo's lives, and the Kelbys begin to feel like they have a family once again. Bayard's "smile/ and his laugh, / and his songs" return, and he feels happy (220). He also makes peace with the land and does not let the hardships of farming unravel him. He no longer stubbornly plants only wheat but instead agrees that he should "try some sorghum, / maybe some cotton, / ...[and] bring the grass back / like Ma wanted" (226). Instead of feeling devastated when his tractor stops working, Bayard "walks behind the team" of mules and gets to know the land again (226). He is willing to try new things, and even help around the house, because he sees his life with new eyes after losing his beloved wife and then almost losing Billie Jo. By making peace with hardship, Bayard transforms his broken life by restarting a family and reimagining his relationship with the land.

Besides making peace with hardship, Bayard transforms his broken life by learning how to be a better parent. Being a better parent enriches Bayard's life and makes him happier, for he helps Billie Jo feel secure in their relationship, and he once again enjoys his daughter's company and can return her love. One way Bayard strengthens his relationship with his daughter is to visit Doc Rice to have his skin spots evaluated. Before Billie Jo runs away, Bayard "didn't care much, / if he had some cancer / and took and died" (209). After his daughter returns and he realizes that he almost lost her, Bayard wants to keep living, and he visits Doc Rice to demonstrate to his daughter that he has not given up on their little family. This response makes Billie Jo feel like she has her father back. Another way Bayard becomes a better parent and brings joy back into his life is his decision to be vulnerable with Billie Jo. After Ma's death, he withdraws from his daughter and stops communicating. After Billie Jo runs away and returns, Bayard realizes that he needs to stop staying silent and instead share himself with his daughter by talking and listening. He tells Billie Jo stories about "when he was a boy" and lets her know that he "dreamed of running off too," although he "didn't have half [her] sauce" (210–211). By sharing with her and paying her this compliment, Bayard helps Billie Jo understand how much love and respect he has for her. In return, she feels reconnected to her father, and the two of them make progress toward rebuilding their relationship. By becoming a better parent, Bayard transforms his and his daughter's shattered life by inviting love back into it.

The tragedy of losing Ma irreversibly changes Bayard Kelby's life. He plunges into a deep depression, and as a result, almost loses his daughter. However, Billie Jo's departure and her return help Bayard turn around his life and begin appreciating it. By making peace with hardship and learning how to be a better parent, Bayard transforms his life by forming a new relationship with Louise, reconnecting with his daughter, and finding a new way to approach his land. Although hardship almost destroys Bayard, it also ironically highlights the value in what and who is still in his life, and he is able to see his land, family, and future with renewed eyes.

Name _____

Date _____ Class _____

Step 3: ToSEEC Explanatory Essay Graphic Organizers

You may refer to the ToSEEC explanatory essay model and use the graphic organizers on the next pages if they help you prepare your thinking before writing. Though each body paragraph organizer has only two evidence rows, you are not limited to two pieces of evidence for each paragraph.

Introduction
Hook
Introduce
Thesis and Preview

Name _____

Date _____ Class _____

ToSEEC Body Paragraph 1 Organizer

Topic Statement:

Evidence: Citation:	**E**vidence: Citation:
Evidence: Citation:	**E**vidence: Citation:

Concluding Statement:

Copyright © 2016 Great Minds®

Name _____

Date _____ Class _____

ToSEEC Body Paragraph 2 Organizer

Topic Statement:	
Evidence: Citation:	**Evidence:** Citation:
Evidence: Citation:	**Evidence:** Citation:
Concluding Statement:	

Copyright © 2016 Great Minds®

Name

Date   Class

Conclusion

Copyright © 2016 Great Minds®

Name _____

Date _____ Class _____

Step 5: EOM Peer Review

Content Review	
Writer of Essay	Reviewer of Essay

1. Does the INTRODUCTION contain a hook? An introduction to the topic and task? A thesis? A preview of the supporting points? Underline and label each part of the introduction on the draft. How could the introduction be improved?

2. Does EACH BODY PARAGRAPH have a topic statement? Circle the topic statement in each paragraph. How could its focus be clearer? How could it support the thesis better?

Name _____

Date _____ Class _____

3. Is textual evidence included and cited in **EACH BODY PARAGRAPH**? Is the evidence relevant? Sufficient? Does it support the topic statement? How could it be improved?

4. Does **EACH BODY PARAGRAPH** provide thorough elaboration of the evidence provided? Underline where you see elaboration. How could it be improved? Overall, does this paragraph support the writer's thesis? How could it be improved?

Name _____

Date _____   Class _____

5. Is there a **CONCLUDING** paragraph? Does it contain the "So What?"? How could the conclusion be improved?

6. Does the essay use a **CAUSE-AND-EFFECT** structure? Label what you see as the "cause" and label what you see as the "effect" being explained. How could this be improved?

7. Does the essay respond to the **PROMPT**? Explain why or why not.

Name _____

Date _____ Class _____

Style and Conventions Review
1. What are some effective **TRANSITIONAL WORDS OR PHRASES** in the draft? Where could a transition word or phrase be added to help guide the reader? Provide paragraph number (1, 2, 3, 4) and suggest a transition.
2. Which paragraph has sentences varied in length and structure? What kind of variety do you see? Where could the writer add more **SENTENCE VARIETY** by combining, changing, or separating sentences? Where could the writer vary the sentence openings?
3. What are some examples of strong and precise **WORD CHOICE**? How could word choice be improved?
4. How effectively does the essay use **FORMAL STYLE**? Look for fragments, imprecise words, and dialect or other informal phrases, and offer alternative suggestions.
5. How effectively does the essay follow the **CONVENTIONS** of standard written English? Note where you see convention, spelling, punctuation, or grammar errors.

Name _____

Date _____ Class _____

Step 7: EOM Explanatory Writing Rubric

Grade 6– Informative/Explanatory Writing

	4 (Exceeds expectations)	3 (Meets expectations)	2 (Partially meets expectations)	1 (Does not yet meet expectations)
Structure	▪ Responds thoroughly to all elements of prompt ▪ Maintains focus on topic throughout piece ▪ Introduces topic ▪ Organizes ideas clearly and effectively ▪ Provides a strong conclusion that follows from and expands on the focus ▪ Uses appropriate transitions to clarify relationships	▪ Responds to all elements of prompt ▪ Maintains focus on topic throughout piece with occasional minor departures ▪ Introduces topic ▪ Organizes ideas clearly and effectively ▪ Provides a conclusion that follows from the focus ▪ Uses appropriate transitions to clarify relationships	▪ Responds to some elements of prompt ▪ Often departs from focus on topic ▪ Introduces topic in an incomplete or unclear way ▪ Organizes ideas inconsistently ▪ Provides a conclusion that is incomplete or may not follow from the focus ▪ Inconsistently uses transitions to connect ideas	▪ Does not respond to prompt; off-topic ▪ Piece lacks focus on topic ▪ Does not introduce topic ▪ Ideas are disorganized ▪ Does not provide a conclusion ▪ Does not use transitions to connect ideas
Development	▪ Develops topic with relevant, sufficient evidence from texts(s) ▪ Elaborates upon evidence thoroughly with accurate, insightful analysis	▪ Develops topic with sufficient, relevant evidence from text(s) ▪ Elaborates upon evidence with accurate analysis	▪ Develops topic with insufficient relevant evidence from texts(s) ▪ Elaborates upon evidence vaguely or superficially	▪ Does not use relevant evidence from text(s) ▪ Does not elaborate upon evidence
Style	▪ Varies sentence patterns for clarity, interest, emphasis and style ▪ Uses precise language and domain-specific vocabulary ▪ Consistently expresses ideas precisely ▪ Establishes and maintains a consistent, formal, and engaging style ▪ Writing shows exceptional awareness and skill in addressing audience's needs	▪ Varies sentence patterns for clarity and interest ▪ Uses domain-specific vocabulary ▪ Mostly expresses ideas precisely ▪ Establishes a formal style, with occasional minor lapses ▪ Writing is appropriate to audience	▪ Varies sentence patterns occasionally for clarity or interest ▪ Uses general vocabulary with a few domain-specific words ▪ Language is occasionally precise and may be unnecessarily wordy ▪ Attempts to use a formal style but with many lapses ▪ Writing is somewhat appropriate to audience	▪ Sentence patterns are basic and repetitive ▪ Uses limited vocabulary inappropriate to the content ▪ Language is imprecise and lacks concision, often wordy or redundant ▪ Uses an inappropriately informal style ▪ Writing is inappropriate to audience
Conventions	Shows strong command of grammar, mechanics, spelling, and usage; errors are minor and few	Shows consistent command of grammar, mechanics, spelling, and usage; occasional errors do not significantly interfere with meaning	Shows inconsistent command of grammar, mechanics, spelling, and usage; some errors interfere with meaning	Does not show command of grammar, mechanics, spelling, and usage; errors significantly interfere with overall meaning and writing is difficult to follow

Copyright © 2016 Great Minds®

Name _____

Date _____ Class _____

Step 7: EOM Checklist

	Self +/ Δ	Peer +/ Δ	Teacher +/ Δ
Structure			
▪ I respond to all parts of the prompt			
▪ I focus on my topic throughout the piece			
▪ I introduce the topic clearly in my introduction paragraph			
▪ My introduction paragraph gives some kind of preview of the rest of the piece			
▪ I organize my ideas clearly in body paragraphs			
▪ My conclusion paragraph supports the focus			
▪ I use transitions to smoothly and logically connect paragraphs and ideas			
Development			
▪ I develop my topic with sufficient evidence from text(s)			
▪ My evidence is relevant to the topic			
▪ I elaborate upon evidence by analyzing it accurately			
Style			
▪ I use a variety of sentence patterns (simple, compound, complex, compound-complex) to add clarity and interest to my writing			
▪ I use vocabulary words that are specific and appropriate to the content			
▪ I write precisely and concisely, without using unnecessary words			
▪ I write in an appropriately formal style			
▪ My writing style is appropriate for the audience			
Conventions			
▪ All of my sentences are complete (no fragments)			
▪ I avoid informal language such as slang			
Total # of checks			

Copyright © 2016 Great Minds®

Name _____

Date _____ Class _____

Handout 30B: Fragments

Directions: Fragments can be long or short, just as complete sentences can be long or short. One way to determine whether a sentence is a fragment is by asking "Guess what?" followed by the words. If the sentence makes sense following "Guess what?", it is a complete sentence. If it does not make sense following "Guess what?", the sentence is a fragment. Try this strategy with the following examples. Label which of each pair is a fragment (F) and which is a sentence (S) and explain how you know.

1. When I have good news. _____

2. I have good news. _____

3. Bud, not Buddy. _____

4. My name is Bud, not Buddy. _____

5. Because the train is still moving. _____

6. The train is still moving. _____

7. I can see far into the distance. _____

8. As far as the eye can see. _____

9. If I had a brother. _____

10. I have a brother. _____

11. I lean out the door and get a real nice breeze. _____

12. Leaning out the door and getting a real nice breeze. _____

Copyright © 2016 Great Minds®

Name

Date   Class

Handout 32A: Experiment with Formal Style II

Directions: Follow the checklist to revise the paragraph below for formal style.

- ✓ Check for fragments using the Guess what? strategy, and change all fragments to complete sentences.

- ✓ Use different types of transitions to show the connection between sentences.

- ✓ Use the most precise words. Avoid overused or boring words (*good, fine, bad, sad, amazing,* and so on).

- ✓ Revise contractions (change *don't* to *do not, couldn't* to *could not,* and so on).

- ✓ Avoid dialect or slang (*ain't, don't got no, whatever,* and so on).

It's hard for Billie Jo to forgive her dad, herself, and even life itself. But when she chooses to forgive, she finds a way to forget the stuff that has made her sad. Forgiveness of all the important things. She's able to get on with her amazing life!

_____

_____

_____

_____

_____

_____

_____

_____

_____

_____

_____

Copyright © 2016 Great Minds®

Volume of Reading Reflection Questions

Resilience in the Great Depression, Grade 6, Module 1

Student Name: _____

Text: _____

Author: _____

Topic: _____

Genre/Type of Book: _____

Share your knowledge about the Great Depression and the experiences that individuals had during this time by answering the questions below.

1. Wonder: Consider the title and cover illustration of this text. What drew you to this book? What made you select it?

2. Wonder: What other questions about the Great Depression or the types of experiences that people had during this time did the text inspire?

3. Organize: Describe the main character or characters. What major problem or challenge did the main character face? How was this problem resolved?

4. Organize: Where there any elements or situation that were difficult to understand? What vocabulary, historical details, or background knowledge would be helpful to know in order to better understand this book?

5. Reveal: What story or situation that the main character experienced gave you deeper insight into the character or the particular challenges that peopled faced during the Great Depression?

Copyright © 2016 Great Minds®

6. Reveal: How did the author's use of language or the story's narrative structure help you make a deeper connection with the story? Provide some examples from the text.

7. Distill: Did the text provide you with any new perspectives on the Great Depression or the experiences that people might have had during this difficult time? Provide at least two new insights you gained.

8. Distill: How did the characters in this book demonstrate the idea of resiliency during the Great Depression.

9. Know: What similarities do you see between the characters in your book and the characters in *Bud, Not Buddy* and/or *Out of the Dust*?

10. Know: What important ideas about resiliency and facing challenges that you learned by reading this text help you better understand?

WIT & WISDOM PARENT TIP SHEET

WHAT IS MY SIXTH GRADE STUDENT LEARNING IN MODULE 1?

Wit & Wisdom is our English curriculum. It builds knowledge of key topics in history, science, and literature through the study of excellent texts. By reading and responding to stories and nonfiction texts, we will build knowledge of the following topics:

Module 1: Resilience in the Great Depression

Module 2: A Hero's Journey

Module 3: Narrating the Unknown: Jamestown

Module 4: Courage in Crisis

In this first module, *Resilience in the Great Depression*, we will study one of the worst economic situations in American history, the Great Depression. We will explore the hardships families faced and the triumphs they endured during the Great Depression.

OUR CLASS WILL READ THESE TEXTS:

Novels

- *Bud, Not Buddy*, Christopher Paul Curtis
- *Out of the Dust*, Karen Hesse

Historical Account

- "The Drought," PBS American Experience
- "Hoovervilles," History.com
- "Hoover's Prodigal Children: Hungry Times on Mean Streets," Errol Lincoln Uys

Poetry

- "Mother to Son," Langston Hughes

Copyright © 2016 Great Minds®

Music

- "It Don't Mean a Thing If It Ain't Got That Swing," Duke Ellington and Irving Mills

OUR CLASS WILL EXAMINE THESE WORKS OF ART:

Photography

- *Kentucky Flood*, Margaret Bourke-White
- *Migrant Mother*, Dorothea Lange

OUR CLASS WILL WATCH THESE VIDEOS:

- "1930s GM Sit-Down Strike," History.com
- "Black Blizzard," History.com
- "Migrant Mother Photo," History.com

OUR CLASS WILL ASK THESE QUESTIONS:

- What makes Bud a survivor?
- What hardships did people face during the Great Depression?
- How is Bud transformed by his journey?
- What sustained people's spirits during the Great Depression?
- How does hardship alter the characters' perspectives in *Out of the Dust*?
- What makes the characters in *Out of the Dust* survivors?
- How can enduring tremendous hardship contribute to personal transformation?

QUESTIONS TO ASK AT HOME:

As your sixth grade student reads, ask:

- *What do you notice and wonder?*

BOOKS TO READ AT HOME:

- *Children of the Great Depression*, Russell Freedman
- *On the Blue Comet*, Rosemary Wells
- *A Long Way from Chicago: A Novel in Stories*, Richard Peck

Copyright © 2016 Great Minds®

- *Moon Over Manifest*, Clare Vanderpool
- *My Side of the Mountain*, Jean Craighead George
- *Sounder*, Williams H. Armstrong
- *Roll of Thunder, Hear My Cry*, Mildred Taylor
- *No Promises in the Wind*, Irene Hunt

PLACES YOU CAN VISIT TO TALK ABOUT THE GREAT DEPRESSION:

Visit a local history museum. Ask if there are any exhibits or artifacts from the Great Depression. As you view them with your learner, ask:

- *What makes someone a survivor?*
- *What do you see here that shows the hardships people faced during the Great Depression?*
- *How can enduring hardship change us?*

Copyright © 2016 Great Minds®

CREDITS

Great Minds® has made every effort to obtain permission for the reprinting of all copyrighted material. If any owner of copyrighted material is not acknowledged herein, please contact Great Minds® for proper acknowledgment in all future editions and reprints of this module.

- *All material from the Common Core State Standards for English Language Arts & Literacy in History/Social Studies, Science, and Technical Subjects* © Copyright 2010 National Governors Association Center for Best Practices and Council of Chief State School Officers. All rights reserved.

- All images are used under license from Shutterstock.com unless otherwise noted.

- Assessment 11: "Mother to Son" by Langston Hughes. Used by permission of Harold Ober Associates Incorporated. Copyright © 1994 by The Estate of Langston Hughes.

- "Mother to Son" from THE COLLECTED POEMS OF LANGSTON HUGHES by Langston Hughes, edited by Arnold Rampersad with David Roessel, Associate Editor, copyright © 1994 by the Estate of Langston Hughes. Used by permission of Alfred A. Knopf, an imprint of the Knopf Doubleday Publishing Group, a division of Penguin Random House LLC. All rights reserved.

- For updated credit information, please visit http://witeng.link/credits.

Copyright © 2016 Great Minds®

ACKNOWLEDGMENTS

Great Minds® Staff

The following writers, editors, reviewers, and support staff contributed to the development of this curriculum.

Ann Brigham, Lauren Chapalee, Sara Clarke, Emily Climer, Lorraine Griffith, Emily Gula, Sarah Henchey, Trish Huerster, Stephanie Kane-Mainier, Lior Klirs, Liz Manolis, Andrea Minich, Lynne Munson, Marya Myers, Rachel Rooney, Aaron Schifrin, Danielle Shylit, Rachel Stack, Sarah Turnage, Michelle Warner, Amy Wierzbicki, Margaret Wilson, and Sarah Woodard.

Colleagues and Contributors

We are grateful for the many educators, writers, and subject-matter experts who made this program possible.

David Abel, Robin Agurkis, Elizabeth Bailey, Julianne Barto, Amy Benjamin, Andrew Biemiller, Charlotte Boucher, Sheila Byrd-Carmichael, Jessica Carloni, Eric Carey, Janine Cody, Rebecca Cohen, Elaine Collins, Tequila Cornelious, Beverly Davis, Matt Davis, Thomas Easterling, Jeanette Edelstein, Kristy Ellis, Moira Clarkin Evans, Charles Fischer, Marty Gephart, Kath Gibbs, Natalie Goldstein, Christina Gonzalez, Mamie Goodson, Nora Graham, Lindsay Griffith, Brenna Haffner, Joanna Hawkins, Elizabeth Haydel, Steve Hettleman, Cara Hoppe, Ashley Hymel, Carol Jago, Jennifer Johnson, Mason Judy, Gail Kearns, Shelly Knupp, Sarah Kushner, Shannon Last, Suzanne Lauchaire, Diana Leddy, David Liben, Farren Liben, Jennifer Marin, Susannah Maynard, Cathy McGath, Emily McKean, Jane Miller, Rebecca Moore, Cathy Newton, Turi Nilsson, Julie Norris, Galemarie Ola, Michelle Palmieri, Meredith Phillips, Shilpa Raman, Tonya Romayne, Emmet Rosenfeld, Jennifer Ruppel, Mike Russoniello, Deborah Samley, Casey Schultz, Renee Simpson, Rebecca Sklepovich, Amelia Swabb, Kim Taylor, Vicki Taylor, Melissa Thomson, Lindsay Tomlinson, Melissa Vail, Keenan Walsh, Julia Wasson, Lynn Welch, Yvonne Guerrero Welch, Emily Whyte, Lynn Woods, and Rachel Zindler.

Early Adopters

The following early adopters provided invaluable insight and guidance for Wit & Wisdom:

- Bourbonnais School District 53 • Bourbonnais, IL
- Coney Island Prep Middle School • Brooklyn, NY
- Gate City Charter School for the Arts • Merrimack, NH
- Hebrew Academy for Special Children • Brooklyn, NY
- Paris Independent Schools • Paris, KY
- Saydel Community School District • Saydel, IA
- Strive Collegiate Academy • Nashville, TN
- Valiente College Preparatory Charter School • South Gate, CA
- Voyageur Academy • Detroit, MI

Design Direction provided by Alton Creative, Inc.

Project management support, production design, and copyediting services provided by ScribeConcepts.com

Copyediting services provided by Fine Lines Editing

Product management support provided by Sandhill Consulting

Copyright © 2016 Great Minds®